A Treasure Cove Story

Based on the Marvel comic book series The Avengers
Adapted by Billy Wrecks
Illustrated by Patrick Spaziante

When Earth is in great danger, the world's mightiest super heroes assemble. Together they are known as...

The Avengers!

This

Treasure Cove Story

belongs to

THE MIGHTY AVENGERS

A CENTUM BOOK 978-1-912396-35-1
Published in Great Britain by Centum Books Ltd.
This edition published 2018.

3 5 7 9 10 8 6 4

Centum Books Ltd, 20 Devon Square, Newton Abbot,
Devon, TQ12 2HR, UK.

www.centumbooksltd.co.uk | books@centumbooksltd.co.uk
CENTUM BOOKS Limited Reg.No. 07641486.

A CIP catalogue record for this book is available
from the British Library.

Printed in China.

Captain America!

Captain America has the strength and speed of
a great athlete. With his unbreakable shield, Captain
America leads the Avengers in their never-ending fight
to defend truth, justice and freedom.

Iron Man!

Iron Man wears armour that allows him to fly
and fire powerful repulsor rays! Iron Man keeps the
Avengers one step ahead of the super criminals who
use advanced technology for their far-reaching plots.

Thor!

Thor can control wind, rain and lightning! When he spins his magical hammer, Thor can fly through the air at amazing speeds.

Hulk!

Hulk is the strongest hero there is! When the
Avengers must face one of their toughest enemies,
Hulk is the green-skinned giant for the job.

The criminal organization called **HYDRA** wants to take over the world! But they will never succeed, because the Avengers will always stand in their way.

The **Wrecker** and the Wrecking Crew are super-strong bullies who think they can take whatever they want, whenever they want it! Luckily, the Avengers have the courage to take them on, any time and any place!

Thor's evil brother, **Loki**, uses magic to try to get his wicked way. Luckily, neither magic nor sinister schemes can overcome the combined courage of the Avengers!

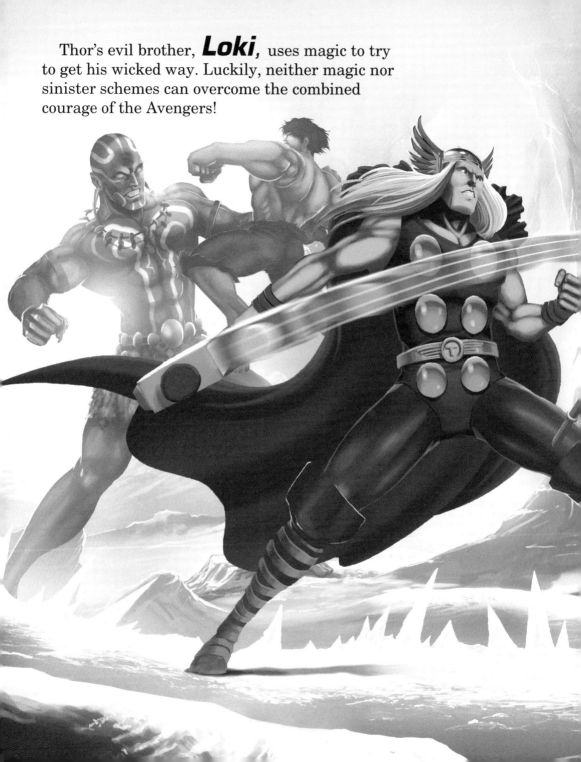

Ultron is an indestructible robot determined to rule the universe! But super science and advanced technology are no match for the might of the Avengers when they use teamwork to face this powerful foe.

After stopping the bad guys, the Avengers take them to a high-tech prison called the Locked Away. The villains can do no more harm, but they're always looking for a way to escape!

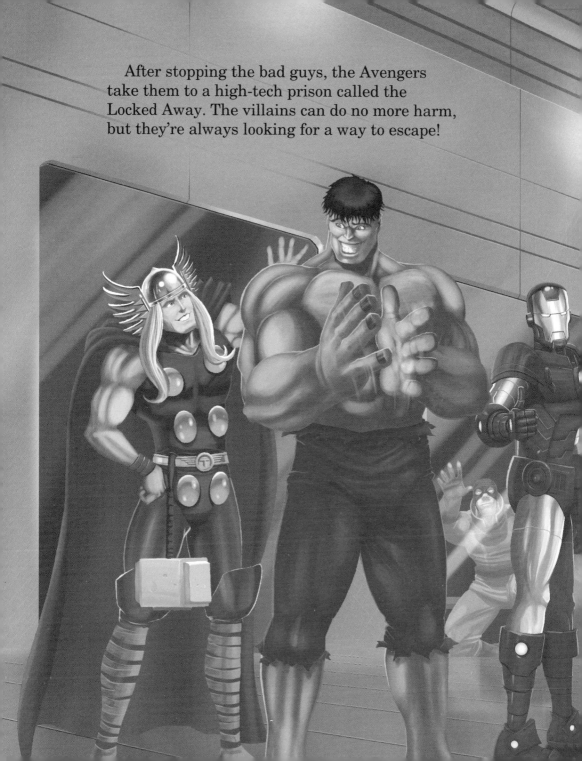

Captain America, Iron Man, Thor and Hulk are amazing heroes on their own. But as the Avengers, their combined super powers are an unstoppable force for good!

Treasure Cove Stories

Please contact Centum Books
to receive the full list of titles in
the *Treasure Cove Stories* series.
books@centumbooksltd.co.uk

Book list may be subject to change. Not all titles are listed.